Hello, I'm Big Cat.
I love to read at
home. What's your name?
Do you like reading too?

Let's read together!
This book is about making the
best of a situation that has not
worked out as you planned.
I hope you enjoy it!

Follow my pawprints after the story
to discover lots of fun things to do.

At the end of the story there's a surprise ...
but wait and see!

If you love reading this book, then please
come and read with me again. There are
lots more exciting things to see and fun
characters to meet!

Published by Collins
An imprint of HarperCollins*Publishers*
77–85 Fulham Palace Road
Hammersmith
London
W6 8JB

Series editor: Cliff Moon

10 9 8 7 6 5 4 3 2 1

ISBN-13 978-0-00-724479-9
ISBN-10 0-00-724479-7

British Library Cataloguing in Publication Data
A Catalogue record for this publication is available from the British Library.

Illustrator: Dee Shulman
Additional illustrators: Clare Beaton, Rachel Bridgen
Design manager: Nicola Kenwood @ Hakoona Matata
Additional designer: Lodestone Publishing Limited; www.lodestonepublishing.com
Guided reading ideas author: Linda Pagett
Education consultant: Dr Rona Tutt

Acknowledgements
Collins would like to thank the teachers and children at the following schools who
took part in the development of Collins Big Cat:

Alfred Sutton Primary School
St. Anne's Fulshaw C of E Primary School
Anthony Bek Primary School
Biddick Primary School
Britannia Primary School
Christ Church Charnock Richard C of E
Primary School
Cronton C of E Primary School
Cuddington Community School
Glory Farm County Primary and
Nursery School

St. John Fisher RC Primary School
Killinghall Primary School
Malvern Link C of E Primary School
Margaret Macmillan Primary School
Minet Nursery and Infant School
Norbreck Primary School
Offley Endowed Primary School
Portsdown Primary School
St. Margaret's RC Primary School
Wadebridge Community Primary School

Printed and bound by Printing Express Limited, Hong Kong

Browse the complete Collins catalogue at **www.collinseducation.com**	Get the latest Collins Big Cat news at **www.collinsbigcat.com**

Woody's Week

my birthday

- Monday
- Tuesday
- Wednesday
- Thursday
- Friday
- Saturday
- Sunday

Written by Michaela Morgan

Illustrated by Dee Shulman

Collins

On Monday I was happy.

On Tuesday I was sad.

love from Gran x

On Wednesday I was happy.

On Thursday I was CROSS!!!

On Friday I had an idea.

On Saturday I made my house.

13

On Sunday we played with my house!

15

Retell the story

Monday

Tuesday

Wednesday

Thursday

Friday

Saturday

Sunday

Encourage your child to follow the days of the week and retell the story. Practise saying the days of the week with and without the words and pictures.

Activities

Why is Woody
happy on Monday?

How does Woody
feel on Tuesday?

How does Woody
feel on Wednesday?

Why is Woody
cross on Thursday?

What happens
on Friday?

What does Woody
do on Saturday?

Activities

Point to the day of the week:

What is the day today?

What was the day yesterday?

Monday
Tuesday
Wednesday
Thursday
Friday
Saturday
Sunday

What is the day tomorrow?

Say each day of the week and what you do on each day.

Use your finger to match the word with how each child is feeling.

happy

sad

angry

excited

surprised

How to make a postbox

You will need:

- A shoebox or a cereal box
- Wrapping paper or hand-decorated paper
- Glue or sellotape
- Scissors
- Paints or colouring pencils (for hand-decorating the paper)

1 Cover the shoebox (box and lid separately) or cereal box (make sure you can still open the top flaps) with the wrapping or hand-decorated paper.

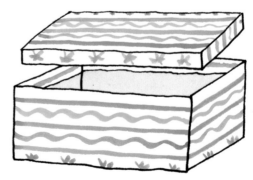

2 Help your child to cut a hole in the lid of the shoebox or the front of the cereal box for the post.

3 Write your name and address on the box. It is now ready for your post!

You can use your postbox for birthday or Christmas cards or any special occasion!

Parents' and carers' notes

Becoming a confident reader can open up a whole new world to your child. Reading should always be fun.

- Look at the cover together and talk about the title and the picture.
- Look at the pictures and see if your child can predict what the story will be about.
- Read the story together, following the words with your finger as you read.
- Look at pages 16–17 and help your child to retell the story in his or her own words.
- Help your child to complete the activities on pages 18–21. These activities revisit the story and give your child an opportunity to talk about what happened.
- Help your child make the postbox on pages 22–23. Discuss what he or she is doing and how he or she is making the box.
- 'Woody's Week' is about relating different feelings to different events, and how to make the best of a situation.

Ask your child to find the following key words and interest words on each page. Help him or her to read the words. Encourage the use of different clues such as the illustrations and initial letters.

Key words: I, was, on, it, we, played, my

Interest words: sad, cross, idea, happy, house, days of the week